GRAPHIC LIBRARY™

GRAPHIC HISTORY

THE VOYAGE OF THE

Mayflower

by Allison Lassieur
illustrated by Peter McDonnell

Consultant:
Walter W. Woodward
Assistant Professor of History
University of Connecticut, Hartford

Raintree

www.raintreepublishers.co.uk
Visit our website to find out
more information about
Raintree books.

To order:
☎ Phone 0845 6044371
🖹 Fax +44 (0) 1865 312263
🖂 Email myorders@raintreepublishers.co.uk

Customers from outside the UK please telephone +44 1865 312262

Raintree is an imprint of Capstone Global Library Limited, a company incorporated in England and Wales having its registered office at 7 Pilgrim Street, London, EC4V 6LB – Registered company number: 6695582

Text © Capstone Press 2006
First published in hardback in the United Kingdom by Capstone Global Library in 2011
Paperback edition first published in 2012
The moral rights of the proprietor have been asserted.

Editorial Director: Blake A. Hoena
Art Director: Jason Knudson
Designer: Jason Knudson
Illustrator: Peter McDonnell
Editors: Rebecca Glaser and John-Paul Wilkins
Originated by Capstone Global Library
Printed and bound in China by South China Printing Company Ltd

ISBN 978 1 406 22559 4 (hardback)
15 14 13 12 11
10 9 8 7 6 5 4 3 2 1

ISBN 978 1 406 22564 8 (paperback)
16 15 14 13 12 11
10 9 8 7 6 5 4 3 2 1

British Library Cataloguing in Publication Data
Lassieur, Allison.
The voyage of the Mayflower. -- (Graphic history)
974.4'8202-dc22
A full catalogue record for this book is available from the British Library.

Disclaimer
All the Internet addresses (URLs) given in this book were valid at the time of going to press. However, due to the dynamic nature of the Internet, some addresses may have changed, or sites may have changed or ceased to exist since publication. While the author and Publishers regret any inconvenience this may cause readers, no responsibility for any such changes can be accepted by either the author or the Publishers.

Editor's note: Direct quotations from primary sources are indicated by a yellow background.

Direct quotations appear on the following pages:
Page 7 (both), from *Of Plymouth Plantation*, William Bradford (Alfred Knopf, 1952.)
Page 11, letter from John Robinson to congregation, printed in *Of Plymouth Plantation*, William Bradford (Alfred Knopf, 1952.)
Page 13, letter from Robert Cushman, printed in *Of Plymouth Plantation*, William Bradford (Alfred Knopf, 1952.)
Page 23, from *Of Plymouth Plantation*, William Bradford (Alfred Knopf, 1952.)

Contents

CHAPTER 1

Plans for a New Life

England had one official church in the early 1600s. If you didn't belong to the Church of England, you were breaking the law. Some groups were willing to worship secretly and risk arrest to practise their own beliefs. One of these groups was the Separatists. They wanted to follow God's word simply, without the extra rules set by the Church of England.

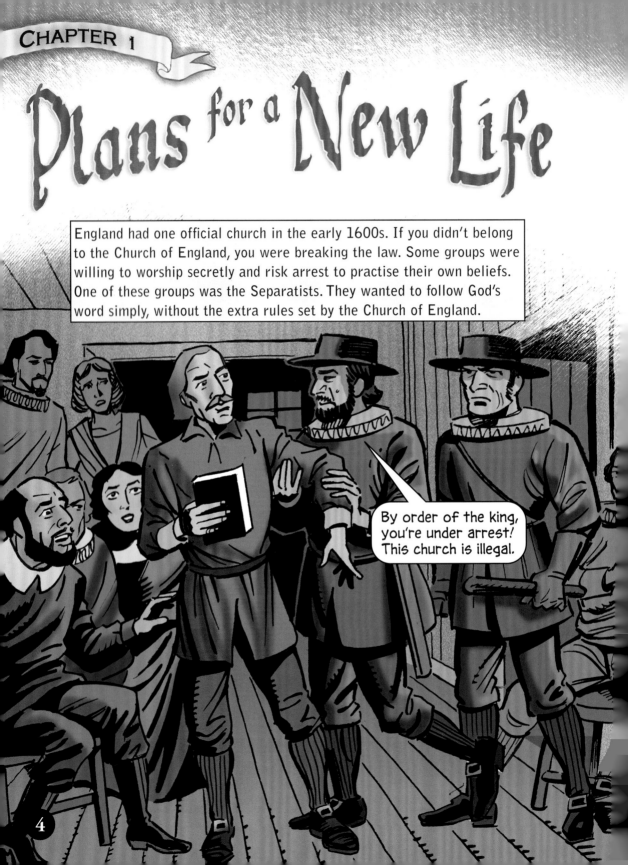

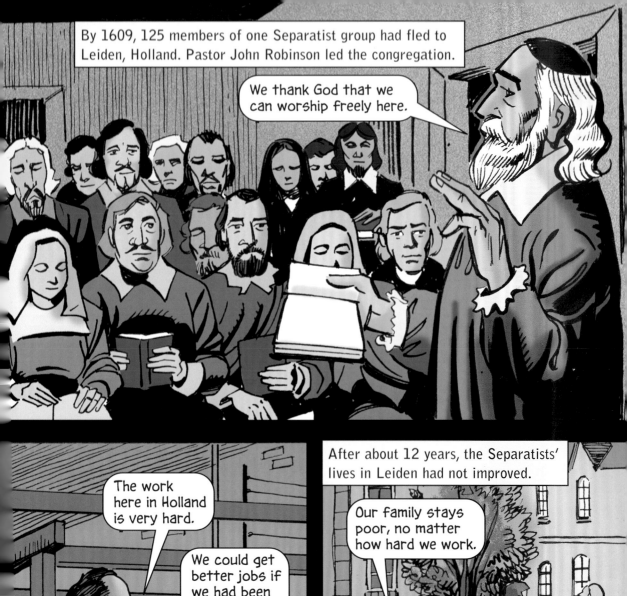

By 1609, 125 members of one Separatist group had fled to Leiden, Holland. Pastor John Robinson led the congregation.

We thank God that we can worship freely here.

The work here in Holland is very hard.

We could get better jobs if we had been born here.

After about 12 years, the Separatists' lives in Leiden had not improved.

Our family stays poor, no matter how hard we work.

Our children now speak more Dutch than English.

The Separatists talked of moving out of Holland. Many in the group, including John Carver, liked the idea.

We can control our own lives in a new land.

But John, how will we provide for our families?

We'll live off the land.

Separatist leaders like Elder William Bradford also wanted to leave.

Elder Bradford, I think we should stay. It's safe here.

It is NOT safe here. Holland may soon be at war with Spain.

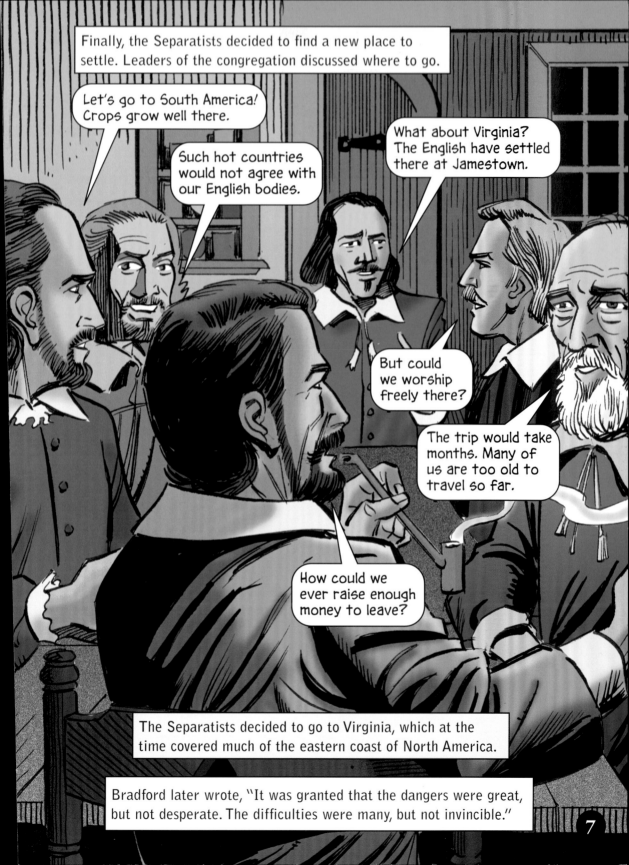

Finally, the Separatists decided to find a new place to settle. Leaders of the congregation discussed where to go.

Let's go to South America! Crops grow well there.

Such hot countries would not agree with our English bodies.

What about Virginia? The English have settled there at Jamestown.

But could we worship freely there?

The trip would take months. Many of us are too old to travel so far.

How could we ever raise enough money to leave?

The Separatists decided to go to Virginia, which at the time covered much of the eastern coast of North America.

Bradford later wrote, "It was granted that the dangers were great, but not desperate. The difficulties were many, but not invincible."

CHAPTER 2

A Troubled Start

The Separatists could not pay for the trip on their own. In London, John Carver and another Separatist, Robert Cushman, made a deal with businessman, Thomas Weston.

Back in Holland, Separatist families sold some of their belongings to pay for the trip.

Mr Cushman, I'll lend you some money for your trip. Your group must come up with the rest.

Thank you, Mr Weston. We'll pay you back in seven years, with lumber and furs from Virginia.

How much can I get for this ring?

Sorry, it's not worth much.

Mother, I could sell my doll.

The Separatists bought a ship in Holland.

The *Speedwell* is a good, solid ship. These sailors will travel with you.

I don't want to go on this dangerous voyage!

Thank you, captain.

Weston will have another ship, the *Mayflower*, meet us in England. We'll take both ships to Virginia.

Weston wanted to make sure the voyage was successful, so he wouldn't lose money. Back in England, he looked for extra passengers. The Separatists called these people the Strangers.

Stephen Hopkins, will you go to the New World?

I'm not a Separatist, but Virginia sounds like a place of opportunity.

9

William Brewster was an elder in the Leiden church. The pastor was staying behind in Leiden, which left Brewster to lead the travelling group. Brewster and his family prepared to leave.

I can't wait to see the ship!

Why are we leaving, Mother?

So we can worship freely and have a better life, son.

While some people were excited to leave, others, such us Bradford's wife, worried about travelling so far.

How will we survive in a land so far from home?

Everything will be all right, Dorothy.

While families packed, Cushman and Carver bought supplies.

This food should be enough for a three-month voyage.

CHAPTER 3

The Mayflower Voyage

After several weeks' delay, the *Mayflower* set sail in good weather on 6 September 1620. Of the 102 passengers, fewer than half were Separatists. The others had come along for different reasons.

Watch where you're going!

Captain Christopher Jones and his crew had been hired to sail the ship. They did not plan to settle in Virginia.

What do you think life will be like in the New World?

Hard work, but think of all the land!

Eighteen people on board the *Mayflower* were servants. They were brought to help clear land and build homes in the New World.

Miles Standish was hired to lead the new colony's military.

Stephen Hopkins was a Stranger from England. He travelled with his pregnant wife, Elizabeth, and their three children.

The *Mayflower* was a cargo ship, not a passenger ship. It had no kitchens. People cooked food over boxes of sand where small fires could be built.

What's for dinner, Mother?

I'm cooking salt pork and cabbage, dear.

The *Mayflower*, like all ships and homes of the time, had no bathrooms. Everyone used small buckets or relieved themselves over the back of the ship.

CHAPTER 4

The New World

On 19 November 1620, the *Mayflower* arrived in the New World.

Land at last!

Praise God! We've arrived safely!

At the end of the voyage, the colonists found themselves far north of Virginia. It was too close to winter to keep sailing, so they landed at Cape Cod, in what is now Massachusetts.

About half the colonists survived the first winter. They built more houses and moved into their new homes. In the spring they met Squanto, a Native American of the Wampanoag people. He spoke English because he had once been kidnapped by English explorers. Squanto helped the colonists survive in the new land.

If you want to grow corn in these old grounds, you must fertilize the fields with fish.

Life in this place might not be so bad after all.

In April, the *Mayflower* and its crew sailed back to England. With Squanto's help, the colonists had a full crop by autumn. They celebrated with a harvest festival Americans now call Thanksgiving.

27

More about the Mayflower

- The people on the *Mayflower* did not call themselves pilgrims. William Bradford first gave that name to the colonists in his book *Of Plymouth Plantation*. Bradford wrote this account during his lifetime, but it was not published until the 1800s.

- The *Mayflower* was built as a cargo ship. Before the ship transported people, it was used to carry wine and furs.

- The original *Mayflower* no longer exists. It is thought that parts of it were later used to build the roof of a barn in Buckinghamshire, England.

- William Mullins, a shoe and boot salesman, brought more than 250 shoes and 13 pairs of boots on the *Mayflower*. He hoped to sell them to the colonists.

- A young passenger named Francis Billington almost set the *Mayflower* on fire. He shot a musket inside a cabin near an open barrel of gunpowder.

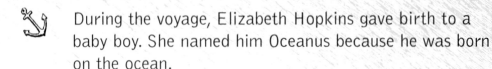 During the voyage, Elizabeth Hopkins gave birth to a baby boy. She named him Oceanus because he was born on the ocean.

Many of the *Mayflower's* passengers got terribly seasick.

Only one person died while the *Mayflower* was at sea. He was a sailor who died from disease.

Passengers on the *Mayflower*:
      50 men
      19 women
      14 teenagers
      19 children (aged 12 and under)

The average age of the men on the *Mayflower* was 34.

Glossary

cargo freight that is carried by a ship

charter document that gives a group the right to create a colony on a certain area of land and provides for a government

contract written agreement between two or more people or groups

elder leader of a religious group who is not a pastor or priest

invincible incapable of being defeated

New World term used by early colonists to refer to North America

plague serious disease that spreads quickly to many people and often causes death

sabotage purposely destroy property to stop an activity

Internet Sites

www.scholastic.com/scholastic_thanksgiving/
This website tells the story of the first Thanksgiving. Follow the *Mayflower's* voyage across the Atlantic on an interactive story map, and learn about daily life in the New World.

www.mayflowerfamilies.com/mayflower/mayflower_passenger_list.htm
On this website, you'll find information about all the passengers who travelled on the *Mayflower*.

Read More

Avoid Sailing on the Mayflower (Danger Zone), Peter Cook (Book House, 2006)

If You Sailed on the Mayflower in 1610, Ann McGovern (Scholastic, 1993)

Mayflower 1620: A New Look at a Pilgrim, Catherine O'Neill Grace and John Kemp (National Geographic Society, 2003)

The Mayflower and the Pilgrims' New World, Nathaniel Philbrick (Puffin Books, 2009)

Bibliography

Of Plymouth Plantation, William Bradford (Alfred Knopf, 1952)

The Mayflower, Kate Caffrey (Stein and Day, 1974)

Mourt's Relation: A Journal of the Pilgrims at Plymouth, G. Mourt (Corinth Books, 1963)

The Pilgrims, Francis Dillon (Doubleday, 1975)

The Times of Their Lives: Life, Love, and Death in Plymouth Colony, James Deetz and Patricia Scott Deetz (W. H. Freeman, 2000)

Index